For Mark, with love L.R.
For Laura, Grace and Oscar L.W.

HODDER CHILDREN'S BOOKS
First published in Great Britain in 2010
by Hodder and Stoughton

Text copyright © Lynne Rickards, 2010
Illustrations copyright © Lee Wildish, 2010

A CIP catalogue record for this book is available from the British Library.

ISBN: 978 1 44494 714 4

1 3 5 7 9 10 8 6 4 2

Printed and bound in China

FSC
www.fsc.org
MIX
Paper from
responsible sources
FSC® C104740

Hodder Children's Books
An imprint of Hachette Children's Group
Part of Hodder and Stoughton
Carmelite House, 50 Victoria Embankment, London, EC4Y 0DZ

An Hachette UK Company
www.hachette.co.uk
www.hachettechildrens.co.uk

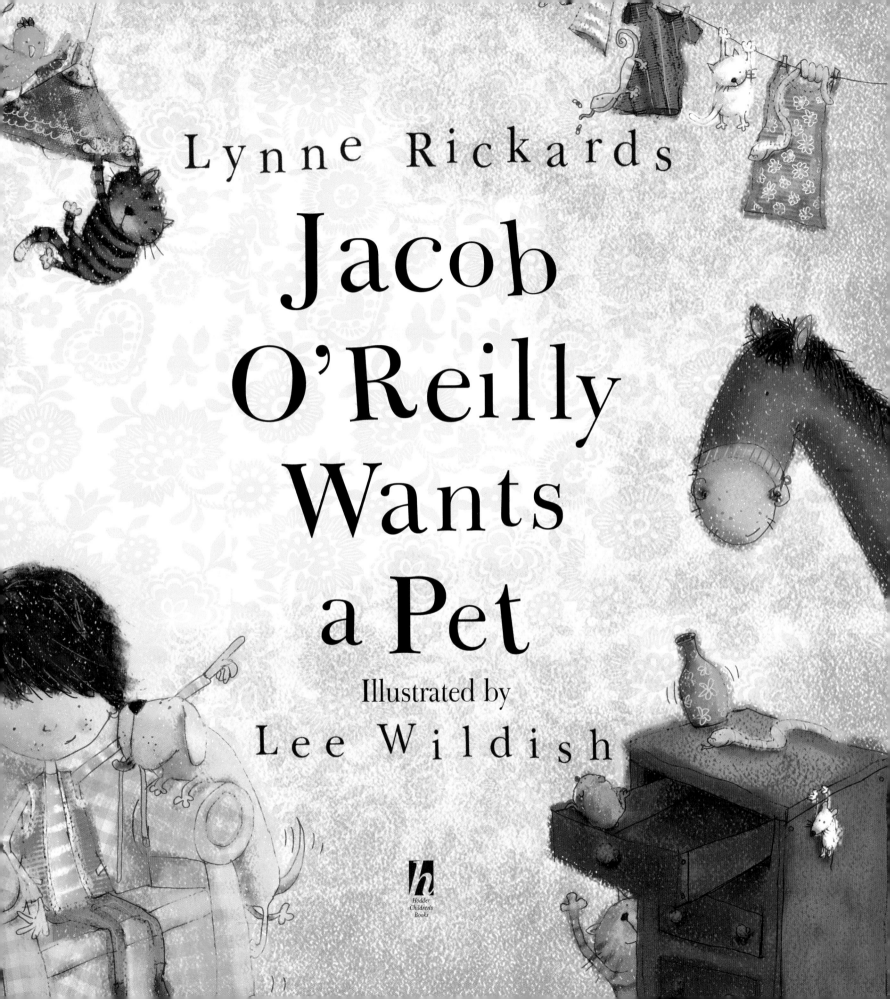

Lynne Rickards

Jacob O'Reilly Wants a Pet

Illustrated by

Lee Wildish

Hodder
Children's
Books

Jacob O'Reilly had tried all he could
to convince Mum and Dad he'd be ever so good –
an absolute angel, the greatest son yet –
if only they'd let him have
one little pet!

He asked for a **dog** but Dad didn't want fleas.
He tried for a **cat** but the fur made Mum sneeze.

He went through a list of small **rodents** for sale,
but the very idea turned Mum and Dad pale.

'If I'm not allowed gerbils
or hamsters or mice,
don't you think an iguana
would be rather nice?

He'd be awfully quiet
and eat all the bugs,
and never leave fur or dead
birds on the rugs...

Oh, PLEASE can I have a pet?'

'An **emu** can make
a fine pet, have you heard?

It is said to be quite an affectionate bird,
and although it is tall and needs quite a large nest,
it keeps to itself and is never a pest...

Oh, **PLEASE** can I have a pet?'

'A **walrus** would be an ideal sort of pet.
He could live in the bathtub to keep himself wet.
I'd comb out his whiskers and scrub his broad back,
and brush those big tusks when he finished a snack...

Oh, PLEASE can I have a pet?'

Well, Mum and Dad thought about all these suggestions while waiting for Jacob to run out of questions.

They pondered their choices and finally said, 'Why not try your own pet-sitting business instead?'

The very next day, Jacob put up a sign:
'Come one and come all! Any number is fine!
I'll care for your pets while you take a nice break.
They'll have a great time here with
Pet-Sitter Jake!'

In no time at all Jacob
had a full house –
four **dogs** and
five **hamsters**,
six **cats** and one
mouse...

A **python** called Morris lay curled on his bed,

two **donkeys**, five **sheep** and one **horse** filled the shed,

the kitchen was hopping
th **rabbits** and **hares**,

and somebody's zebra
was blocking the stairs.

At feeding time Jacob was run off his feet –
some pets wanted salad, and some wanted meat.
They needed a hose-down when dinner was done,
and then it was time for a marathon run!

When two weeks were up and the owners came back,
The house had turned into a flea-bitten shack.
The minute the last pet whizzed off into town,
Pet-Sitter Jake went and pulled his sign down!

And that's when he noticed a rather fine snail,
Just sitting contentedly there on a nail.
'Hello, there,' smiled Jacob, 'I don't think we've met.'
And finally Jacob had found the right pet!

Other great Hodder picture books
perfect to share with children:

978 0 340 95711 0

978 0 340 98868 8

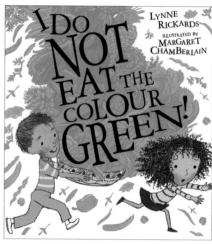

978 0 340 98866 4

978 0 340 98805 3

978 0 340 96000 4

978 0 340 98140 5

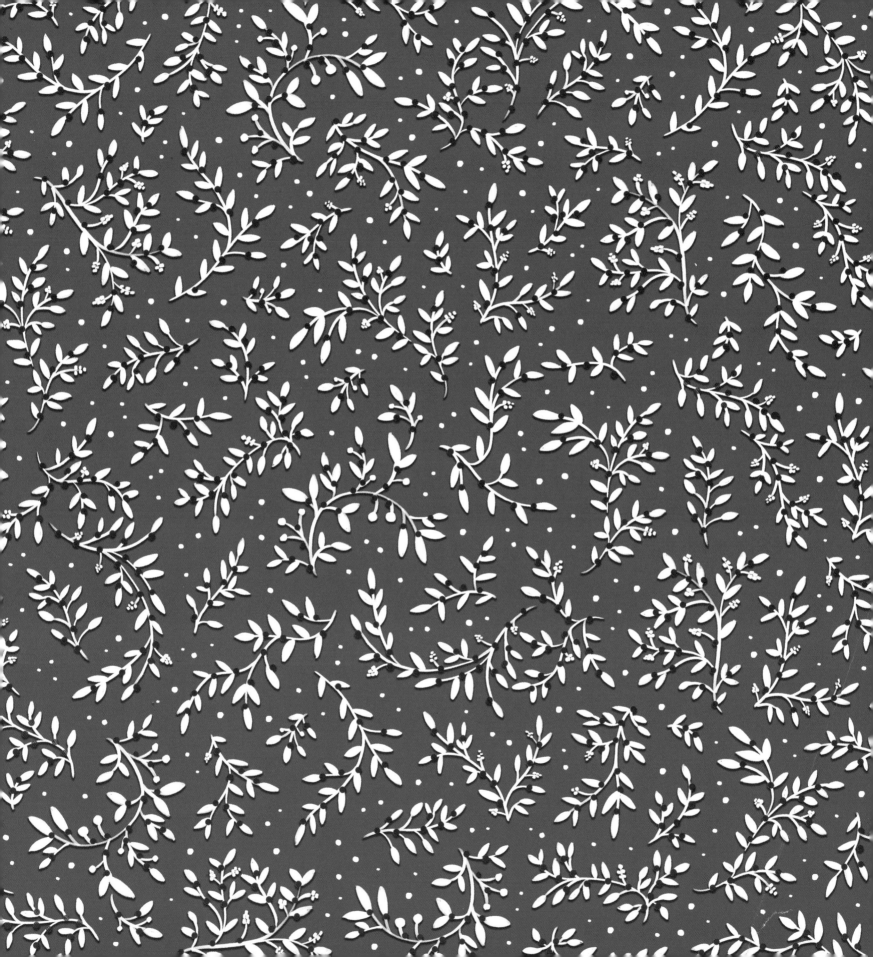

IMAGINE THAT

Licensed exclusively to Imagine That Publishing Ltd
Tide Mill Way, Woodbridge, Suffolk, IP12 1AP, UK
www.imaginethat.com
Design copyright © 2020 Imagine That Group Ltd
Illustration copyright © 2020 Andrea Petrlik/Shutterstock.com
All rights reserved
0 2 4 6 8 9 7 5 3 1
Manufactured in China

Written by Frederic Austin
Illustrated by Andrea Petrlik

ISBN 978-1-78958-727-2

A catalogue record for this book is available from the British Library

The TWELVE days of CHRISTMAS

Illustrations by Andrea Petrlik

1

On the **FIRST DAY** of Christmas,
my true love gave to me ...
A PARTRIDGE IN A PEAR TREE.

On the **SECOND DAY** of Christmas,
my true love gave to me ...
TWO TURTLE DOVES,

And a partridge in a pear tree.

3

On the **THIRD DAY** of Christmas,
my true love gave to me ...
THREE FRENCH HENS,

Two turtle doves,
And a partridge in a pear tree.

4

On the **FOURTH DAY** of Christmas,
my true love gave to me ...
FOUR CALLING BIRDS,

Three French hens,
Two turtle doves,
And a partridge in a pear tree.

5

On the **FIFTH DAY** of Christmas,
my true love gave to me ...
FIVE GOLDEN RINGS,

Four calling birds,

Three French hens,

Two turtle doves,

And a partridge in a pear tree.

6

On the **SIXTH DAY** of Christmas,
my true love gave to me ...
SIX GEESE A-LAYING,

Five golden rings,

Four calling birds,

Three French hens,

Two turtle doves,

And a partridge in a pear tree.

On the **SEVENTH DAY** of Christmas,
my true love gave to me ...
SEVEN SWANS A-SWIMMING,

Six geese a-laying,
Five golden rings,
Four calling birds,
Three French hens,
Two turtle doves,
And a partridge in a pear tree.

8

On the **EIGHTH DAY** of Christmas,
my true love gave to me ...
EIGHT MAIDS A-MILKING,

Seven swans a-swimming,

Six geese a-laying,

Five golden rings,

Four calling birds,

Three French hens,

Two turtle doves,

And a partridge in a pear tree.

On the **NINTH DAY** of Christmas,
my true love gave to me ...
NINE LADIES DANCING,

Eight maids a-milking,

Seven swans a-swimming,

Six geese a-laying,

Five golden rings,

Four calling birds,

Three French hens,

Two turtle doves,

And a partridge in a pear tree.

10

On the **TENTH DAY** of Christmas,
my true love gave to me ...
TEN LORDS A-LEAPING,

Nine ladies dancing,

Eight maids a-milking,

Seven swans a-swimming,

Six geese a-laying,

Five golden rings,

Four calling birds,

Three French hens,

Two turtle doves,

And a partridge in a pear tree.

11

On the **ELEVENTH DAY** of Christmas,
my true love gave to me ...
ELEVEN PIPERS PIPING,

Ten lords a-leaping,
Nine ladies dancing,
Eight maids a-milking,
Seven swans a-swimming,
Six geese a-laying,
Five golden rings,
Four calling birds,
Three French hens,
Two turtle doves,
And a partridge in a pear tree.

12

On the **TWELFTH DAY** of Christmas,
my true love gave to me ...
TWELVE DRUMMERS DRUMMING,

Eleven pipers piping,
Ten lords a-leaping,
Nine ladies dancing,
Eight maids a-milking,
Seven swans a-swimming,
Six geese a-laying,
Five golden rings,
Four calling birds,
Three French hens,
Two turtle doves,
And a partridge in a pear tree.

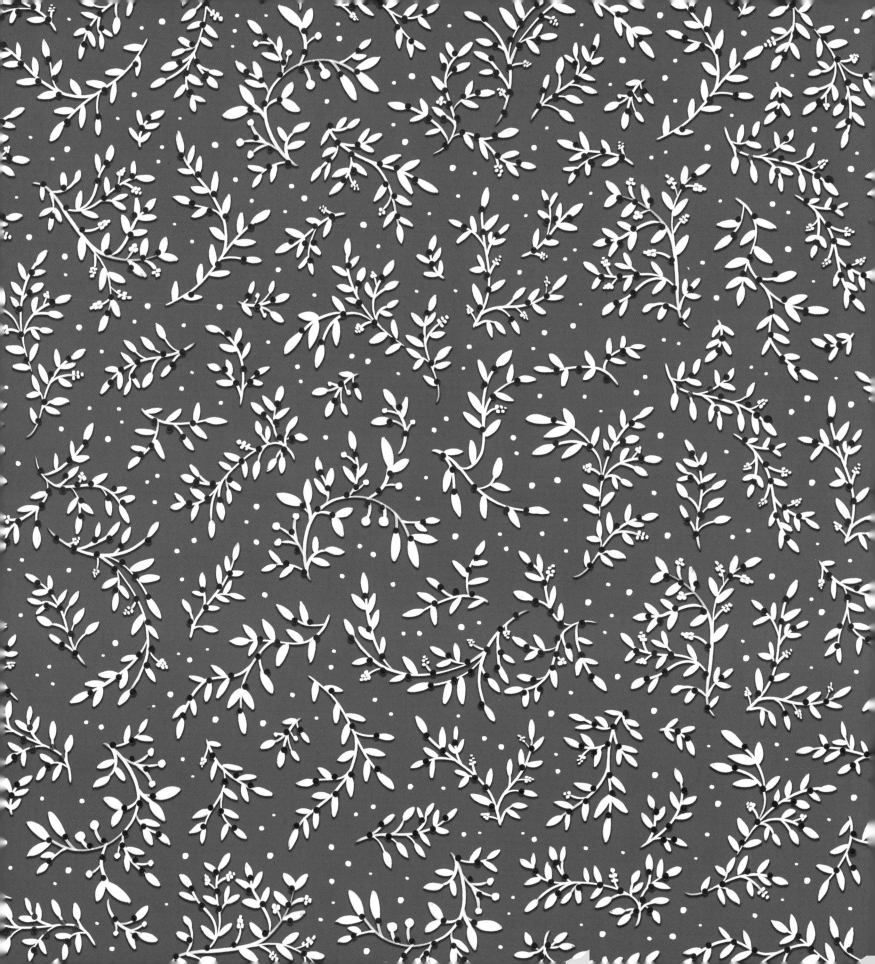